Usborne

Wipe-Clean
Beginning
Pen Control

Use the wipe-clean pen to draw over
all the dotted lines and finish the
shapes and pictures in this book.

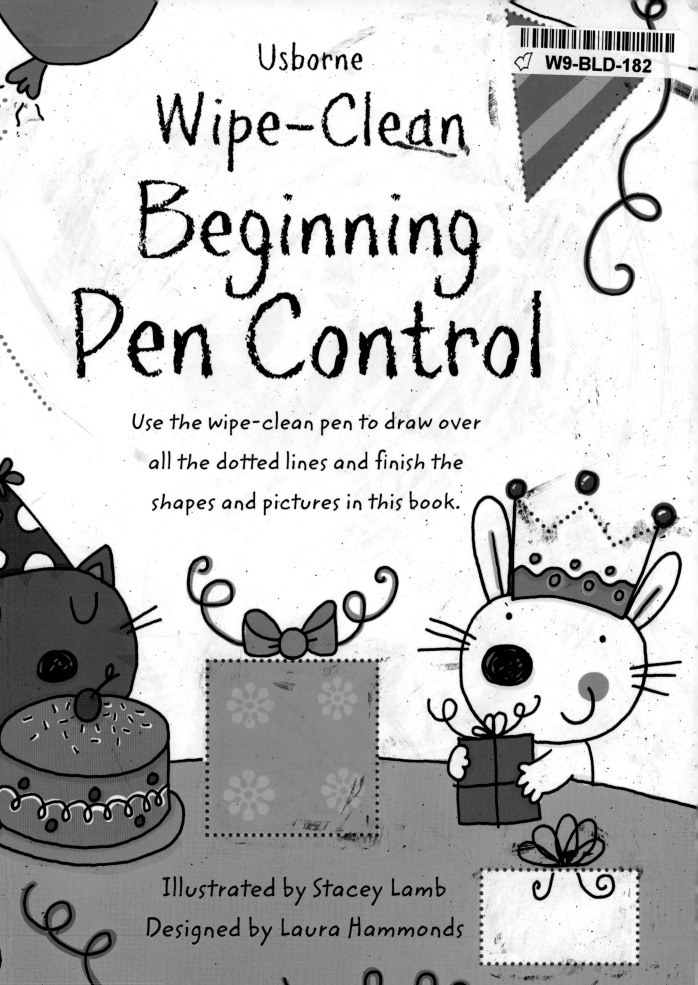

Illustrated by Stacey Lamb
Designed by Laura Hammonds

In the castle

At the train station

On the beach

Out in space

Under the sea

In the park

Snowy day

On the farm

Fireworks at night